Time for a Rhyme

By Ellen Wilkie

Illustrated by Sharon Kane

RAND McNALLY & COMPANY · Chicago

Established 1856

Do you know a word
    That rhymes with TREE?
Turn the page
    And you shall see.

I t's
ME
ME
ME!

Bee Key Knee Sea

Can you think
of a word
That rhymes
with HAT?
I know a word,
It is . . .

CAT

CAT

CAT!

Mat Bat Rat Fat

W hat word do you think
Will rhyme with BOX?
Perhaps the word is . . .

FOX

FOX

FOX!

Socks Clocks Flocks Locks

Let's try to guess
What rhymes
with SPOON
An easy word is . . .

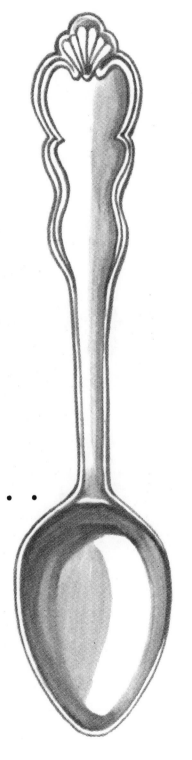

MOON
MOON
MOON!

Lagoon Balloon Racoon Cocoon

Can you say a word
    That rhymes with STAR?
A word I like is . . .

CAR

CAR

CAR!

Far Tar Scar Jar

L et's think of a word
To rhyme with PIE.
I'm sure the word is . . .

SKY
SKY
SKY!

Tie Fly Eye Cry

Can you name a word
That rhymes with MUG?
Let's see if the word is . . .

BUG

BUG

BUG!

Plug Jug Rug Hug

L et's find a word
    That rhymes with zoo
Just take a peek,
    It is . . .

YOU
YOU
YOU!

Stew Dew Blue New

I know a word
    That rhymes with COAT.
Can you guess the word?
    It is . . .

GOAT

GOAT

GOAT!

Boat Note Throat Float

T hink of a word
    To rhyme with CHAIR.
Just make a guess,
    It is . . .

BEAR

BEAR

BEAR!

Hair Stair Wear Fair

Give me a word
    To rhyme with RAIN.
I know for sure it is . . .

TRAIN

TRAIN

TRAIN!

Plane Chain Stain Drain

Let's guess what word
  Will rhyme with TAG.
A simple one is . . .

BAG

BAG

BAG!

Rag Wag Tag Drag

W hat is a word
To rhyme with SLED?
I know, I know, it is . . .

BED

BED

BED!